This book belongs to …

....

Tips for Talking and Reading Together

Stories are an enjoyable and reassuring way of introducing children to new experiences.

Before you read the story:

- Talk about the title and the picture on the cover. Ask your child what they think the story might be about.

- Talk about what nits are. Did you ever have them as a child? Can you remember how you felt?

Read the story with your child. After you have read the story:

- Discuss the Talk About ideas on page 27.

- Talk about the life cycle of a head louse on pages 28-29.

- Do the fun activity on page 30.

Have fun!

Find the snail hidden in every picture.

For more hints and tips on helping your child become a successful and enthusiastic reader look at our website www.oxfordowl.co.uk.

Kipper Gets Nits

Written by Roderick Hunt and Annemarie Young
Illustrated by Alex Brychta

OXFORD

UNIVERSITY PRESS

Kipper was in the garden with Dad, Biff and Chip.
They were watering their sunflowers. Mum was going to
give a prize for the tallest sunflower.

"Dad's sunflower is winning, but only just," said Biff.
"Mum is going to judge them in two weeks, so we've got
time to catch up."

"Kipper keeps scratching his neck," said Chip. "I think he must have fleas."

"It can't be fleas," said Dad.

"But you might have head lice," said Mum. "Try not to scratch."

"Ergh!" said Biff. "That's horrible."

"It's not so horrible," said Mum. "I had head lice when
I was a little girl. It doesn't mean you're dirty. Let me have
a look."

"Hmm," said Mum. "I think I can see some lice and nits. But I'll have to go to the chemist and get a louse comb to make sure."

"If it is head lice we'll have to tell the school," said Mum.

"Sorry!" said Dad, "I forgot. The school sent this letter about nits."

The chemist showed Mum a special kit to get rid of lice. "This is a bug buster kit," he said. "Don't forget to check the whole family."

"We'll have to do some bug busting!" said Mum.
Dad washed the children's hair and put conditioner on it.

Then Mum combed it. Biff didn't have any lice in her hair. But Chip and Kipper did, and the combing got rid of the lice.

Mum plaited Biff's hair tightly to keep it out of the way. "Now I want to see how your sunflowers are doing," said Mum.

14

"They're all quite tall," said Mum.

"But Dad is winning," said Kipper.

"There's still time!" said Mum.

The next day, Kipper got up early. He got the watering can and the plant food and went out to his sunflower. Floppy came out to help.

Kipper put the plant food into the water and gave it to his sunflower. "This should do the trick," he said.

Floppy wagged his tail.

A few days later, after the bug busting, Chip put plant food into the watering can and went out to his sunflower.

He watered his sunflower with the plant food. "This should do the trick," he said.

Floppy wagged his tail.

Later that week, Biff got up early. She watered her sunflower with plant food. "That should do it," she said.

Later, Dad went to check his sunflower. It was taller
than the others, but snails had eaten the leaves, and
the head was droopy!

After two weeks, Mum checked the children's hair.

"Hooray!" she said. "You're all clear of lice and nits."

"Now let's go and check the sunflowers," said Dad.

"I wonder if Dad's is still the tallest?" said Biff.

Dad's sunflower looked twice as tall as the others.

"Aren't I a genius?" asked Dad.

"Oh Dad!" laughed Biff.

"It needed a helping hand," said Dad, "after the snails attacked it."

"That's cheating," said Mum. "No prize for you!"

Mum started measuring the other sunflowers. Floppy started scratching.

"Has he got nits, too?" asked Biff.

"Not nits," said Dad. "Fleas!"

Talk about the story

Why did Mum say getting nits wasn't horrible?

Why do you think Mum wanted to tell the school about Kipper's nits?

How did Mum and Dad get rid of the head lice?

What would you do if you thought you had head lice?

Life cycle of the head louse

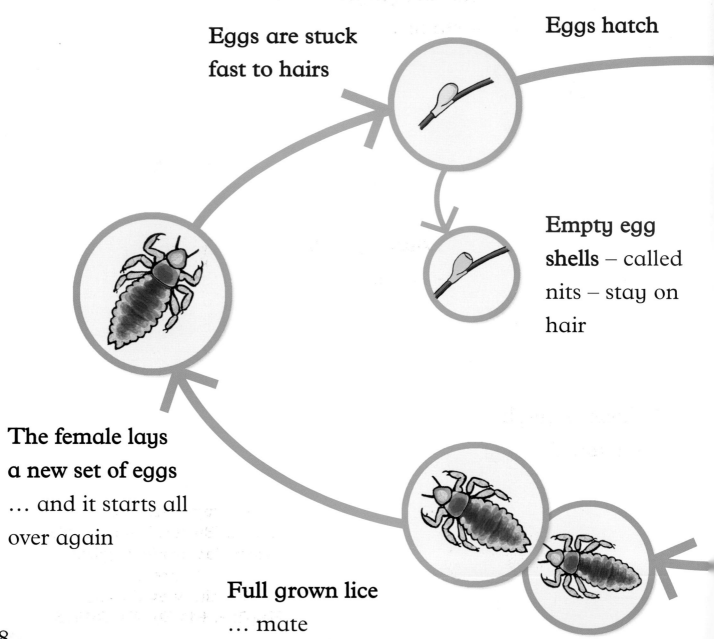

Eggs are stuck fast to hairs

Eggs hatch

Empty egg shells – called nits – stay on hair

The female lays a new set of eggs … and it starts all over again

Full grown lice … mate

Louse nymph
– stage 1

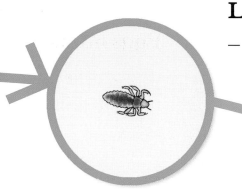

Louse nymph
– stage 2

Louse nymph
– stage 3

Bug Buster Kit
The Bug Buster Kit is available
from Community Hygiene
Concern
Website: www.chc.org
Helpline: +44 (0)1908 561928

Spot the pair

Find the two sunflowers that are exactly the same.

FIRST EXPERIENCES WITH Biff, Chip & Kipper

Have you read them all yet?

Kipper's First Pet

Learning to Swim

Going to the Dentist

Going to the Hairdresser

Going to the Doctor

Going on a Plane

Let's Recycle!

Fun at the Farm

Starting School

Kipper Gets Nits

Going on a Train

FIRST EXPERIENCES Flashcards
55 cards

Also available:
- **At the Hospital**
- **At the Optician**
- **At the Vet**
- **At the Match**
- **At the Dance Class**

Read with Biff, Chip and Kipper
The UK's best-selling home reading series

Phonics   First Stories

Level 1
Getting ready to read

Level 2
Starting to read

Level 3
Becoming a reader

Level 4
Developing as a reader

Level 5
Building confidence in reading

Level 6
Reading with confidence

Phonics stories help children practise their sounds and letters, as they learn to do in school.

First Stories have been specially written to provide practice in reading everyday language.

OXFORD
UNIVERSITY PRESS

Great Clarendon Street, Oxford OX2 6DP
Text © Roderick Hunt and Annemarie
Young 2009
Illustrations © Alex Brychta 2009
First published 2009
This edition published 2013

10 9 8 7 6 5 4 3 2 1
Series Editors: Kate Ruttle, Annemarie Young
British Library Cataloguing in Publication Data available
ISBN: 978-0-19-273513-3
Printed in China by Imago